Section C: **Morality**

Welcome

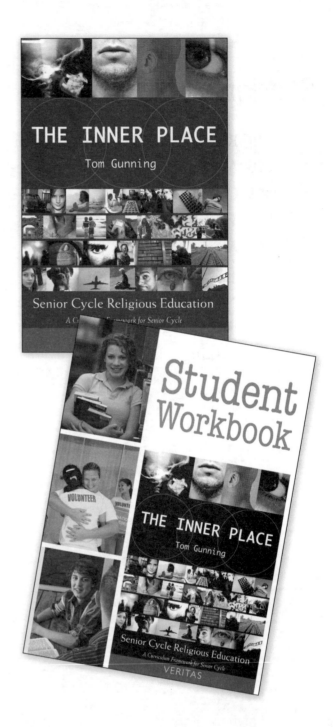

elcome to **The Inner Place** Workbook.

This book looks like a workbook, but is actually much more than that.

It is designed to accompany **The Inner Place** textbook which works through three areas of content: The Search for Meaning, Christianity, and Morality. This workbook aims to help you to reflect at a deeper level on what you are reading about in your textbook.

As you work through the textbook, there will be many questions to discuss with the others in your class. This workbook gives you some starting points for personal reflection on the meaning of what you are learning. It challenges you to ask yourself the question: 'What do the things I am learning and reading about mean for the kind of person I am now and the kind of person I want to become?'; 'Are there any implications for how I should treat the people around me?'; 'What does what I am learning challenge me to value in life and what does it suggest is not worth paying attention to?'; 'Are there things about myself and how I act that I should think about changing?'

You will also be invited to enter your own Inner Place and to be still, so as to discover what God is saying to you right now about yourself as someone made in God's own image and likeness.

There are also suggestions for group exercises and projects which will help you to communicate with the others in your class about the areas you are studying in your textbook.

UNIVERSITY *of* LIMERICK

OLLSCOIL LUIMNIGH

Tel: +353 (0)61 202166 / 202158

Email: libinfo@ul.ie

Web. www.ul.ie/library

You may **borrow** this item by using the self-check machines on the ground floor in the library.
You may **renew** this item by selecting the "My Account" link on the library
catalogue www.ul.ie/library and choose the option " renew loan".
Short Loans may **not** be renewed. Overdue items may incur fines.

Please Note: This item is subject to recall after two weeks if required by another reader.

Workbook

VERITAS

www.veritas.ie

Published 2011 by
Veritas Publications
7–8 Lower Abbey Street
Dublin 1, Ireland
publications@veritas.ie
www.veritas.ie

ISBN 978 1 84730 301 1
Copyright © Veritas, 2011

Designed by Norma Prause-Brewer, Veritas
Printed in the Republic of Ireland by Turners Printing Company
Ltd., Longford.

Veritas books are printed on paper made from the wood pulp of
managed forests. For every tree felled, at least one tree is planted,
thereby renewing natural resources.

Contents

Section B: Christianity

Workbook Guide

📝 **HOW TO USE THE WORKBOOK**

Each worksheet, group work suggestion, prayer exercise or project suggestion references specific pages and sections from the textbook. Ideally, you will have an eye on your textbook as you work through the workbook. What you write in your workbook will be a very useful record for you of your growth and development as a person throughout the year.

This tab references the relevant section from **The Inner Place**.

This tab references the relevant page numbers from **The Inner Place**.

Beginning of exercises

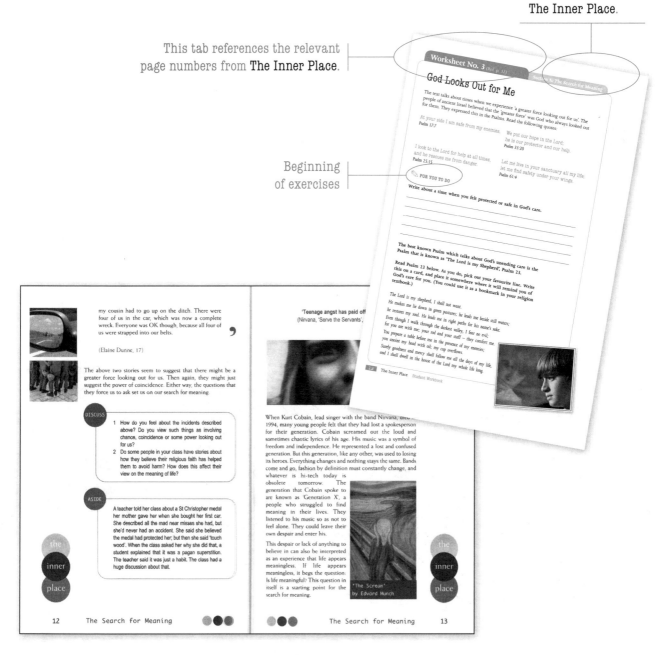

Section A
The Search for Meaning

Making a Difference

You've read about three people who've made a difference in the world.
Have you already had the opportunity to make a difference? How?

✎ **FOR YOU TO DO**

**Think of a situation where you know that something you did
or said made a positive difference to a person or a situation. Write a
few sentences about why you acted as you did, where your motivation
came from and how you think your actions made a difference.**

_____

_____

_____

**As you look at the world around you, who do you see
making a difference for good right now?**

In your own locality

_____

_____

_____

In the wider world

_____

_____

_____

How are they making a difference?

_____

_____

_____

**As you look to the future, where do you think you would like to make
a difference in the longer term?**

_____

_____

_____

The Real Me

Read the following quote from Nelson Mandela.

Our deepest fear is not that we are inadequate. Our deepest fear is that we are powerful beyond measure. It is our light, not our darkness, that frightens us most. We ask ourselves, 'Who am I to be brilliant, gorgeous, talented, and famous?' Actually, who are you not to be? You are a child of God. Your playing small does not serve the world. There is nothing enlightened about shrinking so that people won't feel insecure around you. We were born to make manifest the glory of God that is within us. It's not just in some of us; it's in all of us. And when we let our own light shine, we unconsciously give other people permission to do the same. As we are liberated from our own fear, our presence automatically liberates others.

From Nelson Mandela's 1994 inaugural speech

✎ FOR YOU TO DO

Write about a time when you experienced the 'light within you'.

_____

_____

_____

Write about a time when you experienced the 'darkness within you'.

_____

_____

_____

Nelson Mandela speaks about the glory of God that is within us. Write about a time when you saw the glory of God within someone.

_____

_____

_____

Now, think about how the glory of God is within you. Remember that you are made in the very image of God. Write about your response to this amazing truth and what you think it means for your life.

_____

_____

_____

God Looks Out for Me

The text talks about times when we experience 'a greater force looking out for us'. The people of ancient Israel believed that the 'greater force' was God who always looked out for them. They expressed this in the Psalms. Read the following quotes (taken from the *Good News Bible*):

At your side I am safe from my enemies.
Psalm 17:7

We put our hope in the Lord;
he is our protector and our help.
Psalm 33:20

I look to the Lord for help at all times,
and he rescues me from danger.
Psalm 25:15

Let me live in your sanctuary all my life;
let me find safety under your wings.
Psalm 61:4

 **FOR YOU TO DO**

Write about a time when you felt protected or safe in God's care.

_____

_____

_____

_____

The best known Psalm which talks about God's unending care is the Psalm that is known as 'The Lord is my Shepherd', Psalm 23.

Read Psalm 23 below. As you do, pick out your favorite line. Write this on a card, and place it somewhere where it will remind you of God's care for you. (You could use it as a bookmark in your religion textbook.)

The Lord is my shepherd, I shall not want.

He makes me lie down in green pastures; he leads me beside still waters;

he restores my soul. He leads me in right paths for his name's sake.

Even though I walk through the darkest valley, I fear no evil;
for you are with me; your rod and your staff — they comfort me.

You prepare a table before me in the presence of my enemies;
you anoint my head with oil; my cup overflows.

Surely goodness and mercy shall follow me all the days of my life,
and I shall dwell in the house of the Lord my whole life long.

Finding Something to Believe In

As you explore 'the search for meaning in life', read the three quotes below.

Dream as if you'll live forever, live as if you'll die today.
James Dean (American actor, 1931–1955)

Sometimes it's the smallest decisions that can change your life forever.
Keri Russell (American actress)

Promise me you'll always remember: You're braver than you believe, and stronger than you seem, and smarter than you think.
Christopher Robin to Pooh, by A. A. Milne (English author, creator of Winnie-the-Pooh, 1882–1956)

✎ **FOR YOU TO DO**

Which one appeals to you most?

_____

_____

_____

If you were to take this quote to heart, what difference do you think it would make to your life?

_____

_____

_____

Would it change anything about the way you think about yourself, about others?

_____

_____

_____

_____

Would it change anything about how you act?

_____

_____

Am I a Success or Am I a Failure?

 **FOR THE CLASS TO DO**

Success or Failure?

Divide the class into four groups. Each group will need to collect a large selection of newspapers and magazines.

Using cut-outs of stories and pictures from the papers and magazines, make two displays, one with the heading 'Success in our World' and one with the heading 'Failure in our World'.

List the things that the world rates as success and the things that the world rates as failure.

Now create two further displays, one with the heading 'Success – as God sees it' and one with the heading 'Failure – as God sees it'.

Under each heading, place the stories and pictures which illustrate it. Compare these with the earlier displays.

List the things that are different. What conclusions can you reach from this exercise?

The Importance of My Connections

 **FOR YOU TO DO**

Complete the following diagram, identifying the main connections in your life. One has already been done for you. Then colour each circle red, yellow or blue depending on the level of importance. Red would indicate a very important connection; yellow a connection of medium importance; blue a connection of minor importance. In the space above the diagram, write words that explain how these connections have influenced your life. In the space below the diagrams, write words which explain how these connections have been sustained.

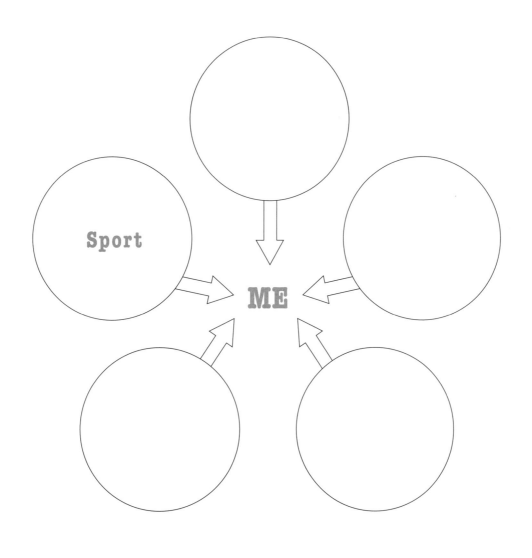

Spirituality for My Life

THINK • PAIR • SHARE

Spend a few moments by yourself. Try to remember what has been the most meaningful spiritual experience you've had in your life to date. Don't forget that it might not have been in a church! Now try to figure out what it was that made that experience so meaningful.

FOR YOU TO DO

Think

Find another person. Share your thoughts.

Pair

Now join with another pair and share your thoughts again.

Share with the class

Share your thoughts with the class. Were there any common threads?

A Sense of Purpose from Involvement in Service

Read the following story

The Story of Jean Donovan

This is a story of how one remarkable woman made the ultimate sacrifice in order to respond to God and live out the message of the Gospel in her life.

Jean Donovan was born in Westport, Connecticut, in 1953 into an upper-middle-class family. After college, she worked as a management consultant in Cleveland and was engaged to a doctor. Though she felt a strong call to motherhood, she also felt that God was calling her to do mission work. As she herself said: 'I sit there and talk to God and say, why are you doing this to me? Why can't I just be your little suburban housewife?'

Jean responded to God's calling and travelled to El Salvador in July 1977, where she worked as a lay missionary along with Dorothy Kazel, an Ursuline nun. They provided help to refugees of the Salvadoran civil war and to the poor. They also provided shelter, food and transportation to medical-care centres, and buried the bodies of the dead left behind by death squads.

Jean admired and was encouraged by the zeal and work of Archbishop Oscar Romero, and she often went to the cathedral to hear him preach. Archbishop Romero was eventually assassinated, on 24 March 1980, for standing up for the Gospel and the poor against the government. Jean and Sister Kazel stood beside his coffin during the night-long vigil of his wake.

In December 1980, Jean and three nuns were to become four more victims, along with the 75,000 others, of the Salvadoran Civil War. On the afternoon of 2 December, Donovan and Kazel, unaware that they were under surveillance by national guardsmen, travelled to the airport in San Salvador to pick up two Maryknoll missionary sisters who were returning from a conference in New York. Acting on orders from their commander, five National Guard members changed into plain clothes and stopped the vehicle they were driving after they left the airport. Jean Donovan and the three sisters were taken to a relatively isolated spot, where the soldiers beat, raped and murdered them.

Early the next morning, local peasants found the bodies of the four women, and were told by local authorities to bury them in a common grave in a nearly field. Four of the local men did so; but they informed their parish priest, and the news reached the local bishop and the US Ambassador to El Salvador the same day. The shallow grave was opened the next day and the bodies exhumed.

In the weeks before she died, Jean Donovan wrote to a friend:

> The Peace Corps left today and my heart sank low. The danger is extreme and they were right to leave … Now I must assess my own position, because I am not up for suicide. Several times I have decided to leave El Salvador. I almost could, except for the children, the poor, bruised victims of this insanity. Who would care of them? Whose heart could be so staunch as to favour the reasonable thing in a sea of their tears and loneliness? Not mine, dear friend, not mine.

 **REFLECT · DISCUSS**

Does Jean Donovan seem to you like someone who had a purpose in life?

Where do you think that sense of purpose came from?

Think of the people you know. Which of them seem to be the ones who really have a purpose in life?

Where does that come from?

Can you recognise any common threads among the lives of those who really seem to have a purpose in life?

What are they? Do you think you would want to have some of these attributes in your own life?

 **FOR THE CLASS TO DO**

Decide on a service project which you and the other students in your class can become involved in. It could involve the entire class group or a smaller group within your class. You will need some time to plan, so you might, for instance, consider something that would happen nearer to Christmas.

You could decide to join in a larger campaign that is being organised by a recognised charity organisation in your locality or in your country.

Or you might consider organising your own service project.

You need to identify a clear target group who will benefit from your project and then establish clear targets as to what you hope to achieve.

Be clear about who does what in the lead-up to whatever action you will eventually take (there will be lots of preparations), as well as during the time when the service project is being carried out.

And then don't forget to evaluate what you achieved. Did you meet your targets?

Consider the Human Response to Evil

The following is an extract from a book by journalist Fergal Keane. The book recalls his experiences of working in various war-torn areas of the world. It is written as a letter to his son, Daniel. The extract here tells of his utter revulsion at the horrors he witnessed in Rwanda, when he set out with a crew to cover the story for British television. It is evidence of one man's recognition of and reaction to evil.

A pity beyond all telling ...

Up ahead is the façade of a church built from red sandstone ... As we drive closer, the front porch of the church comes into view. There is a white marble statue of Christ above the door with hands outstretched. Below it is a banner proclaiming the celebration of Easter, and below that there is the body of a man lying across the steps, his knees buckled underneath his body and his arms cast behind his head. Moses stops the car, but he stays hunched over the wheel and I notice that he is looking down at his feet.

I get out and start to follow Frank across the open ground in front of the church ... As I walk towards the gate, I must make a detour to avoid the bodies of several people. There is a child who has been decapitated and there are three other corpses splayed on the ground.

Closer to the gate Frank lifts a handkerchief to his nose because there is a smell unlike anything I have ever experienced. I stop for a moment and pull out my own piece of cloth, pressing it to my face. Inside the gate the trail continues. The dead lie on either side of the pathway ... I begin to pray myself. 'Our Father, who art in heaven ...' These are prayers I have not said since my childhood, but I need them now ...

Each of us had experienced war and killing before, but in Rwanda we had stepped into a place in which all previous experience of death and conflict paled into insignificance. Here the journalism of objective assessment and rational comparisons meant nothing ... Set against the vastness of the evil of genocide, journalism was, at best, a limited vehicle of expression, at worst a crude and inadequate tool. For how, really, do you convey that sense of evil felt as a physical presence? To walk at night across an overgrown courtyard strewn with the rotting dead, to have to watch every step because in the long grass there are the decapitated heads of the murdered ...

The experience still leaves me struggling for adequate words. To borrow Yeats' phrase, I have started to wonder if the unhinged world I travelled through represented 'a pity beyond all telling'.

(From *Letter to Daniel: Despatches from the Heart* by Fergal Keane, BBC Books, Penguin Books, 1996.)

✤ REFLECT · DISCUSS

How do you think you would have felt had you seen what Fergal Keane saw in Rwanda?

Why do you think Fergal Keane needed to pray in the face of the evil he witnessed?

Has prayer ever helped you at a really difficult time in your life?

What do you think the phrase 'a pity beyond all telling' means?

Making Symbols

As you have read in your textbook, sometimes we want to communicate something to another person and we just cannot find the words to adequately say what it is we want to communicate.

 **FOR YOU TO DO**

Choose a symbol to communicate the following.
It can be an action, a gesture or a thing.

Anger	*Friendship*	*Loneliness*
Love	*Fear*	*Sadness*
Trust	*Happiness*	*Disgust*
Excitement	*Boredom*	*Thankfulness*

Youth Symbols Today

✎ **FOR YOU TO DO**

Name some of the most commonly used youth symbols of today.

_____

_____

_____

_____

_____

_____

For you, what is the most important youth symbol of today? Describe it.

_____

_____

_____

_____

_____

_____

Where does it get its symbolic power from?

_____

_____

_____

_____

_____

_____

Symbols Have Many Meanings

✎ **FOR YOU TO DO**

In the case of the following symbols, what are the different meanings that they can have?

Water	*A Hug*	*A 'thumbs up' sign*
_____	_____	_____
_____	_____	_____
_____	_____	_____
_____	_____	_____
Fire	*A Handshake*	*A Cross*
_____	_____	_____
_____	_____	_____
_____	_____	_____
_____	_____	_____
A Circle	*Light*	*A Seed*
_____	_____	_____
_____	_____	_____
_____	_____	_____
_____	_____	_____
A Flag	*The Colour Purple*	
_____	_____	
_____	_____	
_____	_____	
_____	_____	

Symbols in Your Own Life

✎ **FOR YOU TO DO**

Describe a personal symbol which is important to you.

_____

_____

_____

From where does this symbol get its power in your life?

_____

_____

_____

What is its most important meaning?

_____

_____

_____

In your family

Describe a symbol which is important in the life of your family.

_____

_____

_____

From where did this symbol get its power for your family?

_____

_____

_____

What is its most important meaning?

_____

_____

_____

In your country

Describe a symbol that is important in your country.

_____

_____

_____

From where did this symbol get its power for people in your country?

_____

_____

_____

Why is it important for your country?

_____

_____

_____

With God

Finally, choose a symbol that is significant in terms of your relationship with God. What is this symbol?

_____

_____

_____

Why is it important in terms of your relationship with God?

_____

_____

_____

What is its symbolic meaning?

_____

_____

_____

Where did this meaning come from?

_____

_____

Praying with Symbols

Decide on a time when your class group will spend some time in prayer using symbols. Appoint a group to prepare a Prayer Space for this prayer time. Use some symbolic objects: a lighted candle is often used to remind us of the presence of the Risen Jesus with us at all times; a Cross is a reminder that Jesus suffered and died for each one of us; Holy Water reminds us of our Baptism when we became followers of Jesus and members of the Church. Think of others.

⭐ FOR THE CLASS TO DO

Each one brings in a symbol which for them says something about God's presence with them in their own life, through others, through the world of nature, when they spend time praying alone, or with others, in church or at home.

Gather around the space which has been prepared. Play some quiet reflective music in the background.

Leader: Today we gather to reflect on the many ways in which God is with us. As we look at each one's symbol, we will give thanks for God's presence and pray that we will always be aware of God's closeness to us in our lives.

All: God our Creator, we know you are with us always. In a special way you are with us here today as we gather to pray. Make us ever more aware of your presence as we reflect on the variety of ways you choose to make yourself known to us.

(Each one places his or her symbol in the centre of the group, giving a short description of how it links to God's presence in his or her life.)

Final Prayer

Leader: God our Creator, as we conclude our time of reflection, may we go out enriched with a deeper sense of your presence in our lives, in others around us, in your beautiful creation, whenever two or three are gathered in prayer, in our good times and in our bad times. And may we become for others a source of your presence.

We pray together:

All: Our Father, who art in heaven,
hallowed be Thy Name;
Thy kingdom come,
Thy will be done,
on earth as it is in heaven.

Give us this day our daily bread,
and forgive us our trespasses,
as we forgive those who trespass against us;
and lead us not into temptation,
but deliver us from evil.

Amen.

Water as a Symbol

Water is one of the symbols used in the Sacrament of Baptism.

✎ **FOR YOU TO DO**

Write a short paragraph about why water is an appropriate symbol in Baptism.

_____

_____

_____

_____

_____

_____

Can you think of other situations where water would be an appropriate symbol? Explain why.

_____

_____

_____

_____

_____

_____

Our Beliefs Influence Who We Are

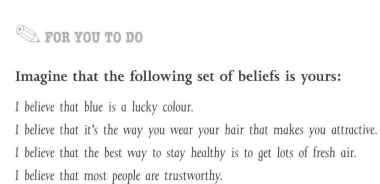 **FOR YOU TO DO**

Imagine that the following set of beliefs is yours:

I believe that blue is a lucky colour.

I believe that it's the way you wear your hair that makes you attractive.

I believe that the best way to stay healthy is to get lots of fresh air.

I believe that most people are trustworthy.

I believe that anyone can succeed at anything if they work hard enough.

I believe that it's easier to get good grades in History than in Geography.

I believe that there's no point in opportunities if you don't make the most of them.

I believe that even when they annoy us, parents want the best for us.

Write a short profile of the person who has these as their beliefs.

_____

_____

_____

_____

_____

_____

Now write down two of your beliefs which you think most influence the kind of person you are. State briefly how they influence you.

1. _____

_____

_____

_____

_____

2. _____

_____

_____

_____

_____

God is Present in Our Lives

 **THINK • PAIR • SHARE**

Think

Think about times in your life when you were aware of God's presence. It may have been in the company of others, your family or friends. It may have been when you were outside enjoying nature. Or perhaps it was a time when you were praying alone or with others. People also sometimes feel a sense of God's presence when they listen to music or look at some work of art. If you have never been aware of God's presence in your life, you can share that too.

Pair

Now find a partner and talk about your experience.

Share

Join with another pair and share what you have spoken about.
What are the common threads that you notice?

Jesus Prayed to God

Jesus also nurtured his relationship with God. In fact, it seems as if he often felt he really needed to be alone with God.

 FOR YOU TO DO

Read the following:
In the morning, while it was still very dark, he got up and went out to a deserted place, and there he prayed.

(Mark 1:35)

After the feeding of the five thousand:
Immediately he made his disciples get into the boat and go on ahead to the other side, to Bethsaida, while he dismissed the crowd. After saying farewell to them, he went up on the mountain to pray.

(Mark 6:45-46)

But now more than ever the word about Jesus spread abroad; many crowds would gather to hear him and to be cured of their diseases. But he would withdraw to deserted places and pray.

(Luke 5:15-16)

Before he chose his twelve apostles:
Now during those days he went out to the mountain to pray; and he spent the night in prayer to God. And when day came, he called his disciples and chose twelve of them ...

(Luke 6:12-13)

What do you think is similar about these instances when Jesus went aside to pray to the Father?

_____

_____

_____

_____

Is there any clue here as to how you might pray?

_____

_____

_____

_____

A Living Spirituality

Christian spirituality is not only concerned with an individual's relationship with God. Spirituality is not only passive, it is active. It has a strong emphasis on a person's actions and interactions with others and with the world. In the Bible this is articulated by the Prophet Micah, 'that you act justly, that you love tenderly, that you walk humbly with your God' (Mic 6:8). Many times in his life Jesus lived out this call in his actions and most particularly in his dealings with others.

✎ **FOR YOU TO DO**

List some incidents that you remember from the Gospels which show Jesus acting as the Prophet Micah says we ought to act.

_____

_____

_____

_____

_____

_____

_____

_____

_____

Now list some times from your own life when you acted in this way.

_____

_____

_____

_____

_____

_____

_____

_____

_____

_____

I Have a Dream

Your textbook takes some time to explore the science of dreaming and how dreams can be interpreted.

We can make a conscious decision to dream about what shape the future will take. There is a theory that if we create images of what our preferred future will be like, we are more likely to make that future a reality. One of the most famous dreams for the future is contained in Martin Luther King Jr's famous 'I have a dream' speech, which was delivered on the steps of the Lincoln Memorial in Washington in 1963. At the time when this speech was delivered, black people were still deprived of many basic human rights in the United States. A very short section from this speech is usually quoted. This is a longer extract which will give you greater insight into what Martin Luther King Jr was actually trying to change.

 **FOR YOU TO DO**

Read the following extract from this speech:

I am happy to join with you today in what will go down in history as the greatest demonstration for freedom in the history of our nation.

Five score years ago, a great American, in whose symbolic shadow we stand today, signed the Emancipation Proclamation. This momentous decree came as a great beacon light of hope to millions of Negro slaves who had been seared in the flames of withering injustice. It came as a joyous daybreak to end the long night of their captivity.

But one hundred years later, the Negro still is not free. One hundred years later, the life of the Negro is still sadly crippled by the manacles of segregation and the chains of discrimination. One hundred years later, the Negro lives on a lonely island of poverty in the midst of a vast ocean of material prosperity. One hundred years later, the Negro is still languishing in the corners of American society and finds himself an exile in his own land …

But we refuse to believe that the bank of justice is bankrupt. We refuse to believe that there are insufficient funds in the great vaults of opportunity of this nation …

We have also come to this hallowed spot to remind America of the fierce urgency of Now … It would be fatal for the nation to overlook the urgency of the moment. This sweltering summer of the Negro's legitimate discontent will not pass until there is an invigorating autumn of freedom and equality. Nineteen sixty-three is not an end, but a beginning …

But there is something that I must say to my people, who stand on the warm threshold which leads into the palace of justice: In the process of gaining our rightful place, we must not be guilty of wrongful deeds. Let us not seek to satisfy our thirst for freedom by drinking from the cup of bitterness and hatred. We must forever conduct our struggle on the high plane of dignity and discipline. We must not allow our creative protest to degenerate into physical violence. Again and again, we must rise to the majestic heights of meeting physical force with soul force …

We cannot walk alone.

And as we walk, we must make the pledge that we shall always march ahead.

We cannot turn back.

There are those who are asking the devotees of civil rights, 'When will you be satisfied?' We can never be satisfied as long as the Negro is the victim of the unspeakable horrors of police brutality … We cannot be satisfied as long as a Negro in Mississippi cannot vote and a Negro in New York believes he has nothing for which to vote. No, no, we are not satisfied, and we will not be satisfied until 'justice rolls down like waters, and righteousness like a mighty stream' …

And so even though we face the difficulties of today and tomorrow, I still have a dream. It is a dream deeply rooted in the American dream.

I have a dream that one day this nation will rise up and live out the true meaning of its creed: 'We hold these truths to be self-evident, that all men are created equal.'

I have a dream that one day on the red hills of Georgia, the sons of former slaves and the sons of former slave owners will be able to sit down together at the table of brotherhood.

I have a dream that one day even the state of Mississippi, a state sweltering with the heat of injustice, sweltering with the heat of oppression, will be transformed into an oasis of freedom and justice.

I have a dream that my four little children will one day live in a nation where they will not be judged by the colour of their skin but by the content of their character.

I have a dream today!

I have a dream that one day, down in Alabama, with its vicious racists, with its governor having his lips dripping with the words of 'interposition' and 'nullification' – one day right there in Alabama little black boys and black girls will be able to join hands with little white boys and white girls as sisters and brothers.

I have a dream today!

I have a dream that one day every valley shall be exalted, and every hill and mountain shall be made low, the rough places will be made plain, and the crooked places will be made straight; 'and the glory of the Lord shall be revealed and all flesh shall see it together.'

This is our hope, and this is the faith that I go back to the South with.

With this faith, we will be able to hew out of the mountain of despair a stone of hope. With this faith, we will be able to transform the jangling discords of our nation into a beautiful symphony of brotherhood. With this faith, we will be able to work together, to pray together, to struggle together, to go to jail together, to stand up for freedom together, knowing that we will be free one day …

And when this happens, when we allow freedom ring, when we let it ring from every village and every hamlet, from every state and every city, we will be able to speed up that day when all of God's children, black men and white men, Jews and Gentiles, Protestants and Catholics, will be able to join hands and sing in the words of the old Negro spiritual:

Free at last! Free at last!

Thank God Almighty, we are free at last!

⭐ FOR THE CLASS TO DO

Why do you think that this speech is considered one of the most inspiring speeches of all time?

Pick out some of the symbolic language contained in it. In what way do you think that the use of symbolic language makes the speech even more powerful?

How do you think this speech might have been significant in black people's struggle for freedom in the United States?

Do you think Martin Luther King Jr's dream also became the dream of his listeners?

How do you think this dream helped the drive for freedom and equality?

In light of this, how do you think your dream for your future can help you shape that future?

Another President's Dream

In your textbook you read about President Abraham Lincoln's dream.

 FOR YOU TO DO

Now read President Barack Obama's dream for his daughters:

Dear Malia and Sasha,

I know that you've both had a lot of fun these last two years on the campaign trail, going to picnics and parades and state fairs, eating all sorts of junk food your mother and I probably shouldn't have let you have. But I also know that it hasn't always been easy for you and Mom, and that as excited as you both are about that new puppy, it doesn't make up for all the time we've been apart. I know how much I've missed these past two years, and today I want to tell you a little more about why I decided to take our family on this journey.

When I was a young man, I thought life was all about me – about how I'd make my way in the world, become successful, and get the things I want. But then the two of you came into my world with all your curiosity and mischief and those smiles that never fail to fill my heart and light up my day. And suddenly, all my big plans for myself didn't seem so important anymore. I soon found that the greatest joy in my life was the joy I saw in yours. And I realised that my own life wouldn't count for much unless I was able to ensure that you had every opportunity for happiness and fulfilment in yours. In the end, girls, that's why I ran for President: because of what I want for you and for every child in this nation.

I want all our children to go to schools worthy of their potential – schools that challenge them, inspire them, and instil in them a sense of wonder about the world around them. I want them to have the chance to go to college – even if their parents aren't rich. And I want them to get good jobs: jobs that pay well and give them benefits like health care, jobs that let them spend time with their own kids and retire with dignity.

I want us to push the boundaries of discovery so that you'll live to see new technologies and inventions that improve our lives and make our planet cleaner and safer. And I want us to push our own human boundaries to reach beyond the divides of race and region, gender and religion that keep us from seeing the best in each other.

Sometimes we have to send our young men and women into war and other dangerous situations to protect our country – but when we do, I want to make sure that it is only for a very good reason, that we try our best to settle our differences with others peacefully, and that we do everything possible to keep our servicemen and women safe. And I want every child to understand that the blessings these brave Americans fight for are not free – that with the great privilege of being a citizen of this nation comes great responsibility. That was the lesson your grandmother tried to teach me when I was your age, reading me the opening lines of the Declaration of Independence and telling me about the men and women who marched for equality because they believed those words put to paper two centuries ago should mean something.

She helped me understand that America is great not because it is perfect but because it can always be made better – and that the unfinished work of perfecting our union falls to each of us. It's a charge we pass on to our children, coming closer with each new generation to what we know America should be.

I hope both of you will take up that work, righting the wrongs that you see and working to give others the chances you've had. Not just because you have an obligation to give something back to this country that has given our family so much – although you do have that obligation. But because you have an obligation to yourself. Because it is only when you hitch your wagon to something larger than yourself that you will realise your true potential.

These are the things I want for you – to grow up in a world with no limits on your dreams and no achievements beyond your reach, and to grow into compassionate, committed women who will help build that world. And I want every child to have the same chances to learn and dream and grow and thrive that you girls have. That's why I've taken our family on this great adventure.

I am so proud of both of you. I love you more than you can ever know. And I am grateful every day for your patience, poise, grace, and humour as we prepare to start our new life together in the White House.

Love, Dad

OVER TO YOU

Imagine that you are one of the two children to whom this was written. What effect do you think it might have on you?

_____

_____

_____

_____

Now in the space provided, write your dream for your own future.

_____

_____

_____

_____

God also has a dream for you and for your future. What do you think that dream is?

_____

_____

_____

_____

God's Dream for the World

What is God's vision for the world?

✎ **FOR YOU TO DO**

In your own words, describe God's dream for the world based on what you have learned from the Bible and Church teachings.

_____

_____

_____

_____

_____

_____

_____

_____

_____

_____

_____

_____

_____

_____

_____

_____

_____

_____

_____

_____

_____

_____

Now consider and write down your ideas on how you could help make this dream a reality.

_____

_____

_____

_____

_____

_____

_____

_____

_____

_____

_____

_____

_____

_____

_____

_____

_____

_____

_____

_____

_____

_____

Section B

Christianity

Section B
Christianity

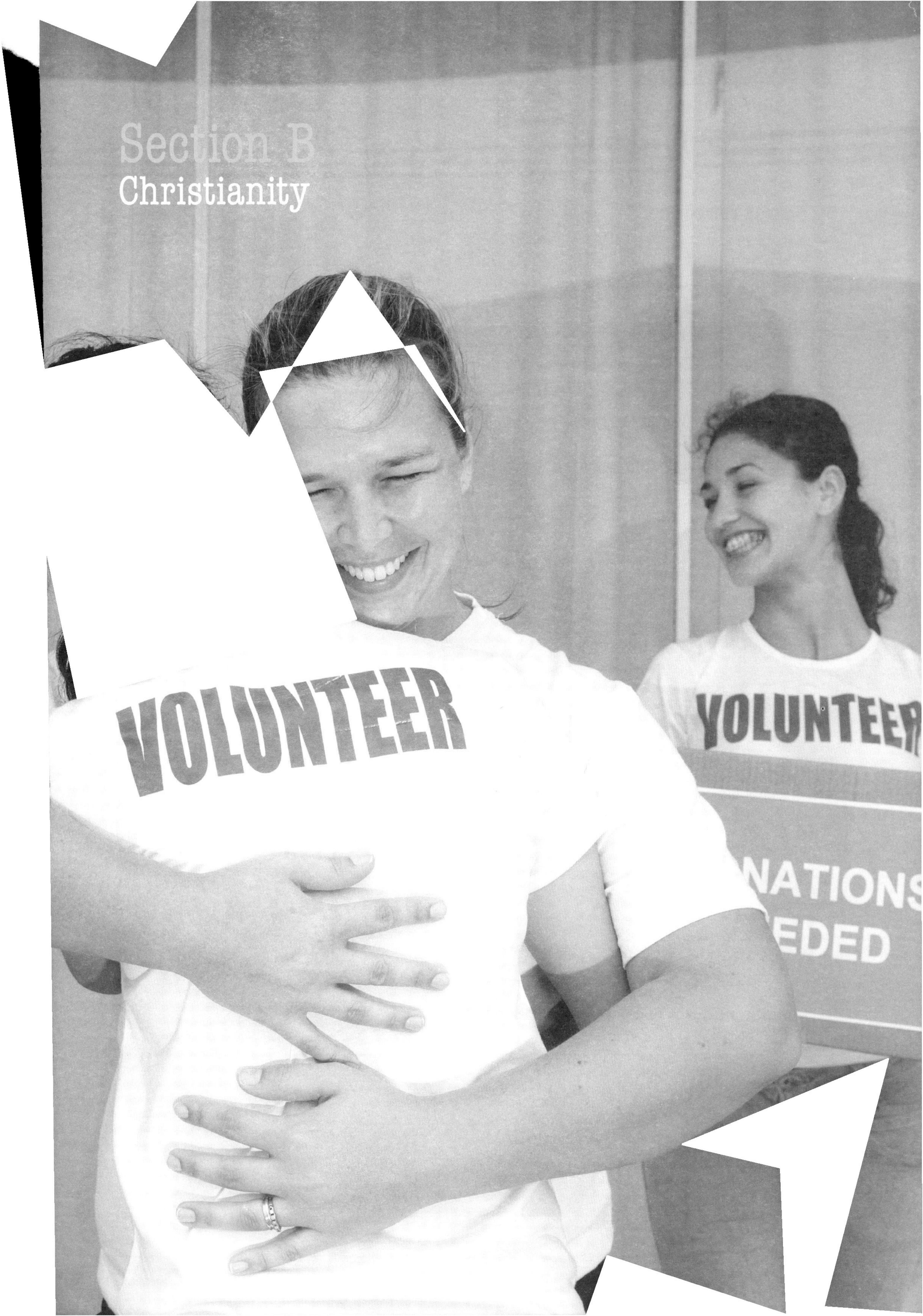

Images of Jesus

✎ **FOR YOU TO DO**

When you think of Jesus, what is the most likely image (picture, painting, statue)to come to mind?

_____

_____

_____

_____

What is it about this image that appeals to you?

_____

_____

_____

_____

What does not appeal to you?

_____

_____

_____

_____

What do you think the artist wanted to convey about Jesus?

_____

_____

_____

_____

Describe an image of Jesus that you like.

_____

_____

_____

_____

If you were to create your own image of Jesus, what qualities do you think you would try to portray?

_____

_____

_____

_____

_____

_____

_____

⭐ FOR THE CLASS TO DO

In groups of four to six, collect all the images of Jesus you can find to make a collage for your classroom wall. They may be pictures, images of statues or word pictures. Use your camera or mobile phone to take pictures of those that are not available in any other way. Try to make sure that your images include some that are modern as well as some that are traditional.

When all of the collages are displayed, try to come up with a caption for the Jesus that is represented in them by your class.

⭐ Class Project

In your group, imagine that you have been commissioned by the local parish to create an image of Jesus to display in the hall of a new primary school. You have been asked to make the image child-friendly. You may use any materials that you wish.

What would you do?

_____

_____

_____

_____

_____

Palestinian Society at the Time of Jesus

 **FOR THE CLASS TO DO**

Form groups of four.

Each individual in that group will represent one of the main groups in Palestine at the time of Jesus.

One person takes on the role of a Pharisee, one a Sadducee, one a Zealot and one an Essene.

Now get together with those who are representing the same group as yourself – all the Pharisees form a group, likewise all the Sadducees, etc. Use the role descriptions given opposite to help you in acting out the role. Discuss what you think of this man Jesus who is walking the roads to Palestine, talking to the people, telling parables, healing those who are sick and, at times, doing things that are not strictly in keeping with the law. Go on to talk about what you think his presence means for the future. What's good and bad about the things he is saying and doing?

Now go back to your original group and discuss your different perspectives on Jesus.

Finally, present to the entire class group the conclusions of the group about Jesus.

Who's Who at the Time of Jesus

The role cards below describe four characters who might have lived at the time of Jesus, one a Pharisee, one a Sadducee, one a Zealot and one an Essene.

Philip the Pharisee

I am a Pharisee, a member of a Jewish religious group. We help to run the synagogues. The most important thing in our lives is God's Law, and all other laws that have been created around that Law. We strictly obey that Law and we want others to do the same. We spend much of our time studying God's Law so that we can guide others in their lives and help them to live the Law in all the details of their lives as well. People have a lot of respect for us because we are people of influence. We help others by pointing out how they can avoid breaking the Law in their everyday lives; for example, by not working on the Sabbath day. We fast regularly and expect everyone else to do the same. Being holy means keeping God's Law and keeping away from those who are sinners. Therefore we teach that those who break the Law are to be avoided at all costs by good religious people. We would like the Roman occupiers to leave our land because they are pagans who do not obey the Law of God. They are a bad influence on the people, but I suppose we have to live with them for the present.

Samuel the Sadducee

I am a priest and I work in the Temple. My father was a priest too, as was his father before him. We are considered to be a very powerful and blessed family because of this. We collect the Temple taxes, which must be paid by everyone who visits the Temple in Jerusalem. This money is used for the upkeep of the Temple and for the support of our families. My family lives well, but that is as it should be. When it comes to the Pharisees … well, they try their best but they are peasants after all, and in some ways they are not strict enough. We try to get along with the Romans because if we didn't they might close the Temple and that would be a disaster for the people and the Jewish religion. It wouldn't do us any good either.

Zachary the Zealot

I try to keep a low profile. It's important that people don't find out too much about me because you never know who will betray you. We Zealots have one goal in mind – to get the Romans out of our country at any cost. We will use any means necessary, including violence, to achieve this goal. After all, the Roman army isn't interested in peaceful methods. We are often called Iscariots, a word that comes from the name given to the small daggers we sometimes use. We try to be good Jews and to keep the Jewish race pure; in other words, we have no time for foreigners. This is God's land and we are God's people. That is what we struggle for.

Jacob the Essene

I was born into the Jewish faith. It means a lot to me. I believe that in order to live a good life I need to separate myself from most of the things that go on in the world every day. I live on the edge of the desert. I seldom meet other people. I spend much of the time praying to God. We would really like to see an end to Roman rule in our country but I don't want to have anything to do with violence and would never join in any military campaign to get the Romans out of our country.

The Kingdom of God

We have spent some time thinking about symbols and how we use them to communicate and to convey meaning.

Jesus also used symbols. The most powerful symbol he used was the symbol of *The Kingdom of God*. A kingdom is usually a territory ruled over by a king or queen. For Jesus, however, the Kingdom of God was not a physical place but a way of being. There are many images detailed in the Gospel of Luke which Jesus used to help people to imagine what life would be like in God's Kingdom. Here are some of them:

A mustard seed
(Luke 13:18-19)

Yeast mixed with flour
(Luke 13:20)

A wedding banquet to which everyone is invited
(Luke 14:15-24)

A woman searching for a lost coin
(Luke 15:8-10)

✎ FOR YOU TO DO

Choose the one which most appeals to you. Write about why this is so.

_____

_____

_____

_____

_____

If you were to choose a symbol to communicate to young people about the presence of the Kingdom of God in the world today, what would it be?

_____

_____

_____

_____

_____

_____

_____

_____

The Beatitudes

✎ **FOR YOU TO DO**

Read the Beatitudes (Matthew 5:1-12).

Which of them do you think you would find most difficult to accept in your own life? For instance, do you think you would feel blessed if you had reason to mourn?

_____

_____

_____

_____

_____

_____

Which of them would you really like to have as an important characteristic in your life?

_____

_____

_____

_____

_____

If these are some of the criteria that Jesus listed as marks of the Kingdom of God, when have you heard a situation described which shows that the Kingdom of God does exist in our world today?

_____

_____

_____

_____

_____

Write Your Own Parable

 GROUP WORK

Form groups of four.
Remember the characteristics of parables:

They have an unusual ending.

There is a reversal of expectation.

The audience becomes emotionally involved.

They play on some bias or prejudice.

They demand that the listeners re-think their world view.

Read the parable of the Good Samaritan again. Now write a modern-day version of this story. Choose locations your audience will recognise. Then choose characters who, in your world, mirror those in the story in terms of how they are regarded by people. When you are finished, listen to each group read its parable to the class.

_____

_____

_____

_____

_____

_____

_____

_____

_____

_____

_____

_____

_____

_____

_____

_____

_____

⭐ **FOR THE CLASS TO DO**

Now with a partner write an original parable.

_____

_____

_____

_____

_____

_____

_____

_____

_____

_____

What expectation needs to be reversed?

_____

_____

_____

_____

_____

_____

_____

What bias needs to be challenged?

_____

_____

_____

_____

_____

_____

_____

The Parables of Jesus

 FOR YOU TO DO

Match each parable with its message.

Parable

Message

The Parable of the Sower Luke 8:4-15

We must treat everyone with kindness, regardless of race, colour, gender, status in society and so on, as every person is our neighbour.

The Parable of the Mustard Seed Luke 13:18

God is loving and merciful and will welcome us back even if we have failed in the past.

The Parable of the Good Samaritan Luke 10:25-37

The Kingdom of God is open to all who wish to share in it by living according to God's will.

The Parable of the Prodigal Son/Loving Father Luke 15:11-32

The coming of the Kingdom of God will be successful despite all obstacles.

The Parable of the Wedding Feast Luke 14:15-24

The Kingdom of God may start very small but it will grow to become the greatest of all kingdoms, where everyone is welcome.

Being Thankful

At the Last Supper, Jesus gave thanks to the Father for all his blessings. The word 'Eucharist' means thanksgiving. Every time we go to Mass we give thanks to God.

How aware are you of all the things you have to be thankful for? It's very easy to take for granted all the things we have that are amazing gifts, that we have done nothing to deserve, that are just ours, like, for instance, the gift of life itself.

It's easy to concentrate on those things in our lives that we wish were different, things that we would like to change. While we do that we can easily forget about all the wonderful blessings we have. Concentrating on the things that are not as good as we would like them to be makes us dissatisfied and unhappy. On the other hand, when we concentrate on the good things in life – and they are there in everyone's life – it can make us happy.

✎ FOR YOU TO DO

Spend a few moments thinking of all the physical gifts for which you can be thankful. Now list them.

_____

_____

_____

_____

_____

Now spend a few moments thinking of all the blessings in your family life that you can be thankful for. List them here.

_____

_____

_____

_____

What about all you have achieved in your life to date? List them here.

_____

_____

_____

_____

Now focus on the gift of friendship. Think of all the wonderful things you get from your friends. List them here.

_____

_____

_____

_____

_____

Spend a few moments thinking of all the other blessings that you have received in life to date. Now write a short prayer of thanks for all you have been given.

_____

_____

_____

_____

_____

_____

_____

_____

_____

_____

_____

_____

_____

_____

_____

_____

_____

_____

Reflection on the Beatitudes

If you think of the word 'Beatitude' as being two words – *be* and *attitude* – you get closer to understanding what the word 'Beatitude' actually means. It means *a way of being in the world* or *an attitude of being*. Now read the reflection below.

Beatitudes
If you can hold great riches
Never letting them hold you;
If you can hear your praises sung
And still give God his due;
If you can help the slow and weak
And raise the one who falls,
And quickly come with helping hand
When anybody calls;
If you can have a heart that's free
From selfishness and sin,
And keep that heart so God's great light
May shine more strongly in;
If you can give forgiveness
To the one who hurts your heart;
If you can build a bridge and bring
Together those apart;
If you can say – this thing is wrong
Or that is right to do,
And stand your ground though other hearts
Would pain and punish you;
If you can be a friend to all,
To all be strong and true,
Then God who made the world
Will make his Kingdom come in you. (Christy Kenneally)

✎ **FOR YOU TO DO**

Ponder the ideas raised in this poem in your heart. What do your answers say about how well-tuned your life is to the values of the Beatitudes?

_____

_____

_____

_____

Living the Beatitudes

 FOR THE CLASS TO DO

Use newspapers, magazines and posters to find images to illustrate each of the Beatitudes being lived out in the world.

Create appropriate captions and assemble the images and captions to make displays for your classroom.

Modern-Day Prophets

Jesus was the last in a long line of prophets sent by God to bring God's message to the people.

⭐ **FOR THE CLASS TO DO**

Together, list all the characteristics of a prophet as outlined in your textbook.

_____

_____

_____

_____

_____

Now think about who the people are in today's world who try to make people aware of those things that need to be changed, in their own lives, in the political world, in relationships between people and groups.

_____

_____

_____

_____

_____

Finally, remember that everyone can take on the role of a prophet. Is there a situation in your own experience right now where you are being called upon to take on the role of a prophet?

_____

_____

_____

_____

_____

⭐ **FOR THE CLASS TO DO**

Using the internet to get information, write up and illustrate the life and work of your chosen modern-day prophet. Then compile a class project on modern-day prophets.

Modern-Day Prophet Sr Dorothy Stang

Jesus was a prophet of his time. In the Bible a prophet was a person who made known to the people what God intended them to hear. Here is the story of a modern-day prophet.

American nun murdered in Brazil for her faith

Silver-haired American nun Dorothy Stang, who has died aged seventy-three after being shot by two gunmen on an Amazon road, looked more like an elderly American holidaymaker than a modern-day martyr. When the two gunmen intercepted her as she walked to a meeting of poor farmers, she must have known what was coming, but she opened her Bible and began reading to them. They shot her six times.

Sr Dorothy had been a worker for the CPT, the Roman Catholic Church's Pastoral Land Commission, since 1982, moving to a small town on the Transamazon Highway. The CPT had been created by the Brazilian bishops in 1975 in response to the mounting violence in the Amazon region, as landowners used gunmen to clear peasant farmers from disputed land. Sr Dorothy's particular interest was in teaching sustainable farming methods to poor settlers, most of whom were unfamiliar with Amazon soils.

Born in Dayton, Ohio, into a large Catholic family, she joined the Sisters of Notre Dame de Namur in 1948 and took her vows in 1956. The Order, founded in France at the end of the eighteenth century, was dedicated to 'taking our stand with poor people, especially women and children in the most abandoned places'.

Like all CPT workers in the Amazon, Sr Dorothy knew her life was threatened. In 2004, although she knew she was putting her life even more at risk, she 'took her stand with poor people', naming logging companies who were invading and destroying state forests. Loggers reacted by calling her a terrorist and accused her of supplying peasant farmers with guns. She and other local leaders began to suffer direct death threats, but she refused to be intimidated and continued her work with the farmers.

Sr Dorothy Stang, nun and activist, born 7 June 1931; died 14 February 2005.

 FOR THE CLASS TO DO

Reflect for a moment on the story of Sr Dorothy Stang.

Now discuss your response to her story.

Why do you think she continued to work in such extreme circumstances?

Now bring some of your thoughts into a class discussion on the impact that people like Sr Dorothy have on our world and, most importantly, on you.

How Do You Pray?

You have just read what Jesus said to his disciples about prayer and how they should pray. There are many ways to pray, and people have suggested ways to help people to pray.

 **FOR YOU TO DO**

This is one idea you might like to try:

Find a quiet place.

Sit comfortably.

Read the following piece of scripture slowly and meditatively.

In those days when there was again a great crowd without anything to eat, he called his disciples and said to them, 'I have compassion for the crowd, because they have been with me now for three days and have nothing to eat. If I send them away hungry to their homes, they will faint on the way – and some of them have come from a great distance.' His disciples replied, 'How can one feed these people with bread here in the desert?' He asked them, 'How many loaves do you have?' They said, 'Seven.' Then he ordered the crowd to sit down on the ground; and he took the seven loaves, and after giving thanks he broke them and gave them to his disciples to distribute; and they distributed them to the crowd. They had also a few small fish; and after blessing them, he ordered that these too should be distributed. They ate and were filled; and they took up the broken pieces left over, seven baskets full. (*Mark 8:2-8*)

Think about what you have read.

Now place yourself in the scene. Who would you like to be? As you imagine yourself in the role of that person, imagine Jesus looking directly at you. What does he say to you? What do you say to Jesus? Read the piece of scripture again. Remember that the Risen Jesus is always with you as you go about your life.

The 'I Am' Statements of Jesus

According to John's gospel, Jesus gave the people seven images of himself. These are known as the seven 'I Am' statements.

I am the Bread of Life
(6:35)

I am the light of the world
(8:12)

I am the gate
(10:9)

I am the good shepherd
(10:11)

I am the resurrection and the life
(11:25)

I am the way, and the truth and the life
(14:6)

I am the vine
(15:5)

✎ FOR YOU TO DO

Which of these best describes Jesus for you?

_____

_____

_____

_____

_____

If you were to write an 'I am' statement for Jesus that you think would speak to young people today, what would it be?

_____

_____

_____

_____

_____

Discuss the images chosen by the different members of the class group.

The Seven Last Words Of Jesus

✎ **FOR YOU TO DO**

Look up the following references and write out the seven last words of
Jesus spoken from the cross. (The Seven Last Words of Jesus refer to
Jesus' final statements on the cross). Which is the most strange? Why?

Luke 23:34   John 19:28   John 19:30

Matthew 27:46   Luke 23:43   John 23:46

John 19:26-27

_____

_____

_____

_____

_____

_____

_____

Which challenges you most? Why?

_____

_____

_____

_____

_____

_____

_____

_____

_____

_____

_____

Persecuted For Their Faith

Group Discussion

The Acts of the Apostles in the Bible show us how the early Christians were prepared to suffer, and even die, for their faith.

✎ **FOR YOU TO DO**

What do you think gave them the courage to do this?

_____

_____

_____

In today's world, what are people prepared to die for?

_____

_____

_____

What do you think it takes for a person to be prepared to die for a cause?

_____

_____

_____

What would you be prepared to die for?

_____

_____

_____

Are there people today who are prepared to die for their faith?

_____

_____

_____

What does this take?

_____

_____

_____

A Letter to the Corinthians

Your textbook talks about St Paul's Letter to the Philippians. Paul also wrote a letter to the people of Corinth, called St Paul's Letter to the Corinthians. This is one of the most famous passages from that letter:

Love is patient; love is kind; love is not envious or boastful or arrogant or rude. It does not insist on its own way; it is not irritable or resentful; it does not rejoice in wrongdoing, but rejoices in the truth. It bears all things, believes all things, hopes all things, endures all things.
Love never ends.
(1 Cor 13:4-8)

✎ FOR YOU TO DO

What piece of this quote affirms the way you most often relate to others?

_____

_____

_____

_____

_____

_____

What piece challenges the way you relate to others?

_____

_____

_____

_____

If you were to choose a phrase as your motto, what would it be?

_____

_____

_____

_____

_____

Section C

Morality

Section C
Morality

Recognising Right from Wrong

✎ **FOR YOU TO DO**

Write about a situation where you recognised that something wrong was taking place and you decided to intervene in order to change or stop what was happening. Say why you did what you did.

_____

_____

_____

_____

Now write about a situation where you recognised that something wrong was taking place and you didn't intervene. Say why you didn't.

_____

_____

_____

_____

Your textbook talks about different ways through which we recognise right from wrong.

From our innate sense of how human beings should behave.

From what the laws of the land tell us about right and wrong.

From what our religion tells us.

Which of these do you think has the most influence on you as you try to figure this out for your own life?

_____

_____

_____

_____

How does this influence operate?

_____

_____

_____

_____

All Actions Have Consequences

 FOR THE CLASS TO DO

Bring into the classroom a bundle of recent newspapers, some local and some national.

Cut out some headlines and some pictures of events. Stick these onto sheets of paper.

Now discuss the events with your group in order to throw light on the consequences of the actions you have highlighted for various individuals and groups, including those who were responsible for the actions in the first place. Don't forget that sometimes the consequences can reach further than you might suspect. Remember that the consequences can be both positive and negative.

Now on the sheets of paper, list the individuals and groups who are affected by the actions you have highlighted.

Finally, each person in your group takes a piece of paper and writes about something she or he has done recently and the consequences it has had for others. Add them to the display.

Conflict of Values

✎ **FOR YOU TO DO**

In the space provided below, write about a time in your life or an incident in which you were involved where you experienced a conflict of values.

_____

_____

_____

_____

_____

_____

_____

_____

_____

_____

_____

_____

Explain the different values which were in operation and say where you think these came from.

_____

_____

_____

_____

_____

_____

_____

_____

_____

_____

Do you think you reached a satisfactory resolution in the end? Explain your answer.

Values in Action

All of us have the power to be a force for good and to help others in difficult situations.

✤ READ · REFLECT

Here is a story about how the creative and loving actions of one man sustained and uplifted another through a time of suffering and illness.

The Hospital Window

Two men, both seriously ill, occupied the same hospital room. One man was allowed to sit up in his bed for an hour each afternoon to help drain the fluid from his lungs. His bed was next to the room's only window. The other man had to spend all his time flat on his back. The men talked for hours on end. They spoke of their wives and families, their homes, their jobs, their involvement in the military service, and where they had been on holiday.

Every afternoon when the man in the bed by the window could sit up, he would pass the time by describing to his roommate all the things he could see outside the window. The man in the other bed began to live for those one-hour periods when his world would be broadened and enlivened by all the activity and colour of the world outside.

The man by the window described how their room overlooked a park with a lovely lake. Ducks and swans played on the water while children sailed their model boats. Young lovers walked arm in arm amidst flowers of every colour, and a fine view of the city skyline could be seen in the distance. As the man by the window described all this in exquisite detail, the man on the other side of the room would close his eyes and imagine the picturesque scene.

One warm afternoon the man by the window described a parade passing by. Although the other man couldn't hear the band, he could see it in his mind's eye.

Days and weeks passed. One morning the day nurse arrived to bring water for their baths, only to find the lifeless body of the man by the window, who had died peacefully in his sleep. She was saddened and called the hospital attendants to take the body away.

As soon as it seemed appropriate, the other man asked if he could be moved next to the window. The nurse was happy to make the switch, and after making sure he was comfortable, she left him alone.

Slowly, painfully, he propped himself up on one elbow to take his first look at the real world outside. He strained to look out the window beside the bed. It faced a blank wall. The man asked the nurse what could have compelled his deceased roommate who had described such wonderful things outside this window. The nurse responded that the man was blind and could not even see the wall. She said, 'Perhaps he just wanted to encourage you.'

What thoughts do you think were going through the mind of the blind man by the window as he described the scenes for his roommate each day?

What words would you use to describe this man?

What values influenced his actions?

OVER TO YOU

Think of times in your life when you have been challenged to overcome your limitations to reach out to others. If you feel comfortable doing so, share your experiences. Say what it was you think influenced your actions.

Acting Morally

✎ **FOR YOU TO DO**

List three moral choices that you remember making

1. _____

_____

2. _____

_____

3. _____

_____

Now list what influenced your choice in each case

1. _____

_____

2. _____

_____

3. _____

_____

Now assess where the most dominant influence comes from in your moral decision making. Some possibilties might be: your family values, your friends and what they might think of what you do, your religion, stories you have read or heard. There may also be other factors not listed here.

_____

_____

_____

_____

_____

_____

_____

_____

_____

The Ten Commandments

These are the Ten Commandments that God gave to Moses on Mount Sinai as they appear in the Book of Exodus:

I am the Lord your God, you shall have no other God but me.
You shall not make wrongful use of the name of the Lord your God.
Remember the Sabbath Day and keep it holy.
Honour your father and your mother.
You shall not murder.
You shall not commit adultery.
You shall not steal.
You shall not bear false witness against you neighbour.
You shall not covet your neigbour's house ... or anything that belongs to your neighbour.

✎ **FOR YOU TO DO**

Which commandment gave directions to the people about how they should behave in their relationship with God?

_____

_____

Which commandment gave directions about the people's relationships with others?

_____

_____

Name two situations where the way you acted was influenced by the commandments.

_____

_____

_____

Which commandments were they and why do you think they influenced what you did?

_____

No Sin is Unforgiveable

In this worksheet we explore how hating someone who has hurt us doesn't take away our pain, and that healing can come through forgiveness.

 **READ · REFLECT**

Here is a story about one woman's battle with pain and loss. In the depths of despair and hurt, Winifred Potenza was able to bring about healing for herself and for the perpetrator of her suffering.

Winifred Potenza's oldest son, Jonathan, aged twenty-one, and his fiancée, Lisa Rodriguez, were killed instantly when their car was struck by a drunken driver. Winifred's grief was unbearable and she often found herself walking the streets late at night sobbing.

The district attorney decided to charge the drunken driver, William, with murder. (The usual charge for such a fatality is manslaughter.) This charge was done under the extreme instigation of Winifred. The twenty-year-old driver pleaded guilty and waived his right to a trial. He was consumed by guilt and wanted to die.

Winifred was instructed to avoid any contact with the young man's family or friends. Sitting in the courtroom when the judge sentenced William to 'fifteen years to life', Winifred really saw William for the first time. In that instant she realised that he was not the monster she had been told he was. She says that she thought, 'Oh, my God, this is wrong.' She realised that William also had parents who loved their son. Winifred rose from her seat and walked right past the guards to give William a hug.

Winifred forgave William and became his friend and advocate. Forgiveness helped them both to heal and it also gave William back the will to live. Winifred began weekly visits to William in prison. She says, 'William is a good person. He has special talents and deserves another chance.'

Winifred worked tirelessly to have William's charges reduced to manslaughter, which would lessen his sentence. Her efforts paid off when it was discovered that William had never signed the document that waived his right to a trial by a jury. The court threw out his conviction. After seven years of imprisonment, William was released on parole.

For Winifred, the death of her son marked the beginning of an ambitious art project that focuses on peace, both personal and global. The project is called *The Hearts of the World*. It consists of a series of paintings on large canvases. Each canvas depicts a heart using design elements from each country's symbol, and colours from its flag. This ongoing project has sent Winifred travelling around the world to deliver the paintings to the leaders of the countries depicted.

Winifred says, 'Tragedy affected me terribly and beautifully. When I am working on *Hearts of the World*, I do it in Jonathan's name and that inspires me.'

(See 'Real Stories Of Forgiveness', www.catherineblountfdn.org)

This story could have ended differently. Winifred's positive action changed the situation from one of pain and loss to one of healing, forgiveness and peace. Can you think of any other examples of stories where positive action helped ease someone's pain and hurt? Share your stories.

In what way does Winifred's actions in this story mirror God's stance toward humanity?

What lessons have you learned from this story for your own life?

Forgiveness

God always forgives us no matter what we do.

In this worksheet we read the story of a woman whose father was killed in an IRA bombing in Brighton, England, during the time of the Troubles in Northern Ireland, and how she coped with her pain by befriending her father's murderer. This story is an example of the triumph of good over evil, and of extraordinary human forgiveness.

❖ READ • REFLECT

When Jo Berry's father, Sir Anthony Berry MP, was killed in an IRA bombing of a British Government convention in Brighton, England, in October 1984, Jo found an extraordinary way out of the darkness. She befriended her father's murderer, IRA bomber Patrick Magee, and together they now work for peace. Here is the story of how the events unfolded:

When the Brighton bomb exploded on 12 October 1984, Jo Berry's life changed in an instant. Her father, Conservative MP Sir Anthony Berry, was among those who died in the bombing. She recalls the time: 'When the bomb went off, it killed my father in such a violent way that I couldn't cope with the pain or the trauma for a long, long time. It took away the free spirit that was me – that part of me had died because I thought, this is actually the real world, the real world is at war, the real world is where people are killed . . . And then there was this incredible need in me to find a way of bringing something positive out of it. I didn't really know what that meant but I knew I couldn't just stay in the horror and the trauma.'

She thinks she first heard the name of Patrick Magee when he was arrested. She couldn't bear to attend the trial. 'I wasn't ready to find out what was going on, so yeah, it was part of the shock.'

The years passed and marriage and three daughters failed to remove the memories. Then in June 1999 she saw a news item reporting on her father's killer being freed from jail. She said later: 'He might be free but I had never felt more trapped.'

But an urge to understand the conflict had already led her to Ireland itself. There, among other casualties of the conflict, she found people who understood her pain. 'It was the first time I went somewhere where I knew it was safe for me to open up and feel whatever I was feeling without people saying, "Isn't it time you let go?"'

Now she felt the urge to understand Magee himself, to ask him: 'Why?' She met people claiming to be able to introduce her to him. Eventually . . . the call came one morning.

'My first thought was, no, it's the wrong day, I'm not ready, I'm not feeling inspired, I'm just feeling really mundane and just not in the mood . . . And then another voice came into my head, "You can trust, it is the right time." So I decided to go and meet him and just trust that it would happen.

'We started speaking as soon as we met each other. And there was a moment about halfway through when it changed, and went from Pat justifying and explaining his political beliefs which led him to join the IRA, to Pat taking off his political hat and saying, "I want to hear your pain and your anger and I don't know anymore who I am. What can I do?"

'That's when I knew that it wasn't a one-off meeting, that he had a need to meet me as I had a need to meet him. I didn't realise quite where it would go but I did know we were on a journey and we were going to travel together.'

Now they work together, speaking in conflict zones around the world, and they have set up an organisation called 'Building Bridges for Peace'. They aim to help others in similar situations by telling their stories, and in other ways too, such as providing guidelines for such encounters between victims and perpetrators of violence.

DISCUSS

What is your reaction to Jo's story?

How do you think what she did changed the situation for her?

How did it change the situation for Patrick Magee?

Have you ever been forgiven by anyone? How did it feel?

Making a Difference

The Story of Peter Maurin

With his friend and fellow activist Dorothy Day, Peter Maurin (1877–1949) co-founded the *Catholic Worker*, a newspaper as well as a popular movement characterised by simple living, pacifism and non-violent social change inspired by Catholic social teachings.

Maurin was born in southern France. As a young man he spent time as a teacher, a religious brother and a Catholic community-organiser. At the age of thirty-two, Maurin left France, moving first to Canada and then to the United States. He worked at a variety of jobs – wandering handyman, lumberjack, miner, migrant farm-worker. For Maurin, living simply, with little money, was a gift; it gave him time to study and to think about how society could be reorganised so that 'it would be easier for people to be good'. Maurin began to make frequent visits to New York City, where he stayed in low-cost hotels and shared his ideas with passersbys at street corners and in public libraries.

In 1932 Peter met Dorothy Day, with whom he discussed history – not just presidents, wars and revolutions, but the lives of holy men and women, the stories of people who had worked to make the world a better place. Maurin decided that his greatest task was to support Dorothy in creating the *Catholic Worker*, through which they could put their ideas into practice. The newspaper was launched on 1 May 1933, in the depths of the Great Depression in the United States (1929–39). Maurin wrote numerous 'Easy Essays' for the paper, in which he discussed his Catholic vision for the world. For Maurin, the practice of hospitality was key. For him, 'hospitality' meant opening our hearts and our homes to people in need. 'Modern society,' he wrote, 'calls the beggar [a] bum and [a] panhandler . . . But the Greeks used to say that people in need are ambassadors of the gods.'

Along with the newspaper, Peter and Dorothy helped create two 'Houses of Hospitality' in New York City, and a farm in Pennsylvania where the needy could live and work. All the money to support these endeavours came from individual, personal donations. Even today, the Catholic Worker movement does not accept internet donations or government funding. The members just pray every day with great trust in God and with the confidence that God will provide.

The Catholic Worker movement is grounded in a firm belief in the God-given dignity and generosity of every human person. Today, over 185 Catholic Worker Houses of Hospitality and Worker Farms across the world remain committed to non-violence, voluntary poverty, prayer and hospitality for the homeless, exiled, hungry and forsaken. Catholic Workers continue to protest against injustice, war, racism and violence of all kinds, and many publish newspapers or newsletters to promote and develop Peter and Dorothy's ideas.

With a partner, read the following 'Easy Essay' by Peter Maurin, one of many such essays published in the *Catholic Worker*.

Choose one or two of the arguments expressed in it and discuss your response to them.

Then share some of your best conclusions with the rest of the class.

Better or Better Off?

The world would be better off,
  if people tried
  to become better.

And people would
  become better
  if they stopped trying
  to be better off.

For when everybody tries
  to become better off,
  nobody is better off.

But when everybody tries
  to become better,
  everybody is better off.

Everybody would be rich
  if nobody tried
  to be richer.

And nobody would be poor
  if everybody tried
  to be the poorest.

And everybody would be
  what he ought to be
  if everybody tried to be
  what he wants
  the other fellow to be.

Notes

Notes